The Kahlil Gibran Diary for 1975

THE KAHLIL GIBRAN
DIARY FOR 1975

ALFRED A. KNOPF

NEW YORK

This diary belongs to

Janet Paton

With affectionate good wishes for a happy and
fruitful 1975, full of joy, satisfaction,
and pleasant surprises.

John

JANUARY						
Mon	Tue	Wed	Thu	Fri	Sat	Sun
		1	2	3	4	5
6	7	8	9	10	11	12
13	14	15	16	17	18	19
20	21	22	23	24	25	26
27	28	29	30	31		

MAY						
Mon	Tue	Wed	Thu	Fri	Sat	Sun
			1	2	3	4
5	6	7	8	9	10	11
12	13	14	15	16	17	18
19	20	21	22	23	24	25
26	27	28	29	30	31	

FEBRUARY						
Mon	Tue	Wed	Thu	Fri	Sat	Sun
					1	2
3	4	5	6	7	8	9
10	11	12	13	14	15	16
17	18	19	20	21	22	23
24	25	26	27	28		

JUNE						
Mon	Tue	Wed	Thu	Fri	Sat	Sun
						1
2	3	4	5	6	7	8
9	10	11	12	13	14	15
16	17	18	19	20	21	22
23	24	25	26	27	28	29
30						

MARCH						
Mon	Tue	Wed	Thu	Fri	Sat	Sun
					1	2
3	4	5	6	7	8	9
10	11	12	13	14	15	16
17	18	19	20	21	22	23
24	25	26	27	28	29	30
31						

JULY						
Mon	Tue	Wed	Thu	Fri	Sat	Sun
	1	2	3	4	5	6
7	8	9	10	11	12	13
14	15	16	17	18	19	20
21	22	23	24	25	26	27
28	29	30	31			

APRIL						
Mon	Tue	Wed	Thu	Fri	Sat	Sun
	1	2	3	4	5	6
7	8	9	10	11	12	13
14	15	16	17	18	19	20
21	22	23	24	25	26	27
28	29	30				

AUGUST						
Mon	Tue	Wed	Thu	Fri	Sat	Sun
				1	2	3
4	5	6	7	8	9	10
11	12	13	14	15	16	17
18	19	20	21	22	23	24
25	26	27	28	29	30	31

SEPTEMBER

Mon	Tue	Wed	Thu	Fri	Sat	Sun
1	2	3	4	5	6	7
8	9	10	11	12	13	14
15	16	17	18	19	20	21
22	23	24	25	26	27	28
29	30					

OCTOBER

Mon	Tue	Wed	Thu	Fri	Sat	Sun
		1	2	3	4	5
6	7	8	9	10	11	12
13	14	15	16	17	18	19
20	21	22	23	24	25	26
27	28	29	30	31		

NOVEMBER

Mon	Tue	Wed	Thu	Fri	Sat	Sun
					1	2
3	4	5	6	7	8	9
10	11	12	13	14	15	16
17	18	19	20	21	22	23
24	25	26	27	28	29	30

DECEMBER

Mon	Tue	Wed	Thu	Fri	Sat	Sun
1	2	3	4	5	6	7
8	9	10	11	12	13	14
15	16	17	18	19	20	21
22	23	24	25	26	27	28
29	30	31				

New Year's Day: January 1st

Kahlil Gibran's Birthday: January 6th (1883)

Lincoln's Birthday: February 12th

Ash Wednesday: February 12th

St. Valentine's Day: February 14th

Washington's Birthday: February 17th

St. Patrick's Day: March 17th

Palm Sunday: March 23rd

Passover: March 27th

Good Friday: March 28th

Easter Sunday: March 30th

Mother's Day: May 11th

Memorial Day: May 26th

Father's Day: June 15th

Independence Day: July 4th

Labor Day: September 1st

Rosh Hashanah: September 6th

Yom Kippur: September 15th

Columbus Day: October 13th

Veterans Day: October 27th

Halloween: October 31st

Election Day: November 4th

Thanksgiving Day: November 28th

Channukah: November 29th

Christmas Day: December 25th

The Present Need

Be not heedful of the morrow, but rather gaze upon today, for sufficient for today is the miracle thereof.

Be not overmindful of yourself when you give but be mindful of the necessity. For every giver himself receives from the Father, and that much more abundantly.

The week of December 30th *to* January 5th

Monday

Tuesday

Wednesday

The week of December 30th *to* January 5th

Thursday

Friday

The week of December 30th *to* January 5th

Saturday

Sunday

The Other Person

Your most radiant garment is of the other person's weaving;
  Your most savory meal is that which you eat at the other person's table;
  Your most comfortable bed is in the other person's house.
  Now tell me, how can you separate yourself from the other person?

The week of January 6th to January 12th

Monday

Tuesday

Wednesday

The week of January 6th *to* January 12th

The week of January 6th *to* January 12th

Saturday

Sunday

{ The Desire for Happiness }

Heaven did not decree that I pass my days crying out in agony in the night, saying: "When will come the dawn?" and when the dawn came, asking: "When will end this day?" It was not decreed that man should be unhappy and wretched, for in his depths is created the desire for happiness, because in a man's happiness God is glorified.

The week of January 13th *to* January 19th

Monday

Tuesday

Wednesday

The week of January 13th *to* January 19th

Thursday

Friday

The week of January 13th *to* January 19th

The Music of the Spheres

My soul counseled me and charged me to listen for voices
  that rise neither from the tongue nor the throat.
Before that day I heard but dully, and naught save clamor
  and loud cries came to my ears;
But now I have learned to listen to silence,
To hear its choirs singing the songs of ages,
Chanting the hymns of space, and disclosing the secrets
  of eternity.

The week of January 20th *to* January 26th

The week of January 20th *to* January 26th

The week of January 20th *to* January 26th

The Coming of Spring

All things shall melt and turn into songs when Spring comes. Even the stars, the vast snowflakes that fall slowly upon the larger fields, shall melt into singing streams. When the sun of His face shall arise above the wider horizon, then what frozen symmetry would not turn into liquid melody? And who among you would not be the cupbearer to the myrtle and the laurel?

The week of January 27th *to* February 2nd

Monday

Tuesday

Wednesday

The week of January 27th *to* February 2nd

Thursday

Friday

The week of January 27th *to* February 2nd

Saturday

Sunday

Trust

I saw a companionship between man and all creation;
    And flights of birds and butterflies drawing nigh to
him in safety,
    And gazelles flocking to the pool, trusting.

The week of February 3rd *to* February 9th

Monday

Tuesday

Wednesday

The week of February 3rd *to* February 9th

Thursday

Friday

The week of February 3rd *to* February 9th

Saturday

Sunday

The Wise Dog

One day there passed by a company of cats a wise dog.

And as he came near and saw that they were very intent and heeded him not, he stopped.

Then there arose in the midst of the company a large, grave cat and looked upon them and said, "Brethren, pray ye; and when ye have prayed again and yet again, nothing doubting, verily then it shall rain mice."

And when the dog heard this, he laughed in his heart and turned from them, saying "O blind and foolish cats, has it not been written and have I not known and my fathers before me, that that which raineth for prayer and faith and supplication is not mice but bones."

The week of February 10th *to* February 16th

Monday

Tuesday

Wednesday

The week of February 10th *to* February 16th

Thursday

Friday

The week of February 10th *to* February 16th

The Lost Sheep

And He looked at me and said, "You do not play upon your flute this day. Whence is the sorrow in your eyes?"

And I answered, "A sheep from among my sheep is lost. I have sought her everywhere but I find her not. And I know not what to do."

And He was silent for a moment. Then He smiled upon me and said, "Wait here a while and I will find your sheep." And He walked away and disappeared among the hills.

After an hour He returned, and my sheep was close beside Him. And as He stood before me, the sheep looked up into His face even as I was looking. Then I embraced her in gladness.

And He put His hand upon my shoulder and said, "From this day you shall love this sheep more than any other in your flock, for she was lost and now she is found."

And again I embraced my sheep in gladness, and she came close to me, and I was silent.

But when I raised my head to thank Jesus, He was already walking afar off, and I had not the courage to follow Him.

The *week of* February 17th *to* February 23rd

The week of February 17th to February 23rd

Thursday

Friday

The week of February 17th *to* February 23rd

God Within

You invoke the unknown,
And the unknown clad with moving mist
Dwells in your own soul.
Yea, in your own soul your Redeemer lies asleep,
And in sleep sees what your waking eye does not see.
And that is the secret of our being.

The week of February 24th to March 2nd

Monday

Tuesday

Wednesday

The *week of* February 24th *to* March 2nd

Thursday

Friday

The week of February 24th *to* March 2nd

Saturday

Sunday

The *week of* March 3rd *to* March 9th

Monday

Tuesday

Wednesday

The week of March 3rd *to* March 9th

Thursday

Friday

The week of March 3rd *to* March 9th

War

One night a feast was held in the palace, and there came a man and prostrated himself before the prince, and all the feasters looked upon him; and they saw that one of his eyes was out and that the empty socket bled. And the prince inquired of him, "What has befallen you?" And the man replied, "O prince, I am by profession a thief, and this night, because there was no moon, I went to rob the money changer's shop, and as I climbed in through the window I made a mistake and entered the weaver's shop, and in the dark I ran into the weaver's loom and my eye was plucked out. And now, O prince, I ask for justice upon the weaver."

Then the prince sent for the weaver and he came, and it was decreed that one of his eyes should be plucked out.

"O prince," said the weaver, "the decree is just. It is right that one of my eyes be taken. And yet, alas! both are necessary to me in order that I may see the two sides of the cloth that I weave. But I have a neighbor, a cobbler, who has also two eyes, and in his trade both eyes are not necessary."

Then the prince sent for the cobbler. And he came. And they took out one of the cobbler's two eyes.

And justice was satisfied.

The week of March 10th *to* March 16th

The week of March 10th *to* March 16th

Thursday

Friday

The week of March 10th *to* March 16th

Sunday

The Curse

An old man of the sea once said to me, "It was thirty years ago that a sailor ran away with my daughter. And I cursed them both in my heart, for of all the world I loved but my daughter.

"Not long after that, the sailor youth went down with his ship to the bottom of the sea, and with him my lovely daughter was lost unto me.

"Now, therefore, behold in me the murderer of a youth and a maid. It was my curse that destroyed them. And now on my way to the grave I seek God's forgiveness."

This the old man said. But there was a tone of bragging in his words, and it seems that he is still proud of the power of his curse.

The week of March 17th *to* March 23rd

Monday

Tuesday

Wednesday

The week of March 17th *to* March 23rd

Thursday

Friday

The week of March 17th *to* March 23rd

Saturday

Sunday

One may not reach the dawn save by the path of the night.

The week of March 24th to March 30th

Monday

Tuesday

Wednesday

The *week of* March 24th *to* March 30th

Thursday

Friday

The week of March 24th *to* March 30th

Saturday

Sunday

Tears and Laughter

Upon the bank of the Nile at eventide, a hyena met a crocodile and they stopped and greeted one another.

The hyena spoke and said, "How goes the day with you, sir?"

And the crocodile answered, saying, "It goes badly with me. Sometimes in my pain and sorrow I weep, and then the creatures always say, 'They are but crocodile tears.' And this wounds me beyond all telling."

Then the hyena said, "You speak of your pain and your sorrow, but think of me also for a moment. I gaze at the beauty of the world, its wonders and its miracles, and out of sheer joy I laugh even as the day laughs. And then the people of the jungle say, 'It is but the laughter of a hyena.'"

The week of March 31st to April 6th

Monday

Tuesday

Wednesday

The week of March 31st to April 6th

Thursday

Friday

The week of March 31st *to* April 6th

Saturday

Sunday

The Water of Life

And how else can it be? In grove and in bower when the
rain dances in leaves upon the hill; when snow falls, a
blessing and a covenant; in the valley when you lead your
flocks to the river; in your fields where brooks, like silver
streams, join together the green garment; in your gardens
when the early dews mirror the heavens; in your meadows
when the mist of evening half veils your way—in all these
the sea is with you, a witness to your heritage, and a claim
upon your love.

The week of April 7th to April 13th

Monday

Tuesday

Wednesday

The week of April 7th *to* April 13th

Friday

The week of April 7th *to* April 13th

Saturday

Sunday

The Cry of the Spirit

I say unto you that every day your spirits cry out and in the night do your hearts in their anguish call for succor. But you do not hearken to your spirits and your hearts, for a dying man cannot hear the rattle of death within him; but those who sit by his bed hear. The slaughtered bird dances his fantastic dance without direction of will and knows not; but the beholders know. At what hour of the day sigh not your spirits in agony? Is it in the morning hour, when the love of existence calls you and tears from off your eyes the veil of sleep and leads you to the fields as slaves? Is it at noon, when you would sit in the shade of a tree to protect yourselves against the burning sun, yet cannot? Or at eventide, when you return hungry to your dwellings and find naught save dry bread and clouded water? Or at nightfall, when weariness throws you upon your stone couch and gives you fretful slumber; when you close your eyes in sleep only to awake in fright, imagining the voice of the Shaikh still ringing in your ears? In what season of the year do your hearts not weep in sorrow? Is it in the spring, when nature puts on her new garments and you go out to meet her in your tattered raggedness? Or is it in the summer, when you reap the harvest and gather in the yield to the threshing floor and fill the bins of your lord and master with plenty and receive as your reward only straw and tares? Or in the autumn, when you gather the fruit and press the grapes in the wine-press and receive naught of it except vinegar and acorns? Or yet in the winter, when the elements oppress you and the cold drives you into your snow-covered huts, while you sit within on the hearth crouching and fearful of the raging storms? This is then your life, my poor brethren. This is the night drawing over your souls, unfortunate ones. These are the shadows of your wretchedness and misery. This is the cry of anguish which I heard arising out of your depths so that I awoke and rebelled against the monks and their way of life, and stood alone, complaining in your name and in the name of justice, which suffers your sufferings.

The week of April 14th to April 20th

Monday

Tuesday

Wednesday

The week of April 14th *to* April 20th

Thursday

Friday

The week of April 14th *to* April 20th

Saturday

Sunday

❖ *Come and Follow Me* ❖

Then He looked into my eyes and gazed into the depths of my heart. And He said, "I have chosen you and your brother, and you must needs come with me. You have labored and you have been heavy-laden. Now I shall give you rest. Take up my yoke and learn of me, for in my heart is peace, and your soul shall find abundance and a home-coming."

When He spoke thus, I and my brother stood up before Him, and I said to Him, "Master, we will follow you to the ends of the earth. And if our burden were as heavy as the mountain we would bear it with you in gladness. And should we fall by the wayside we shall know that we have fallen on the way to Heaven, and we shall be satisfied."

The week of April 21st *to* April 27th

Monday

Tuesday

Wednesday

The week of April 21st to April 27th

Thursday

Friday

The week of April 21st *to* April 27th

Saturday

Sunday

The week of April 28th to May 4th

Monday

Tuesday

Wednesday

The week of April 28th *to* May 4th

Thursday

Friday

The week of April 28th *to* May 4th

Saturday

Sunday

Love's Secret

Love triumphs.
The white and green of love beside a lake,
And the proud majesty of love in tower or balcony;
Love in a garden or in the desert untrodden,
Love is our lord and master.
It is not a wanton decay of the flesh,
Nor the crumbling of desire
When desire and self are wrestling;
Nor is it flesh that takes arms against the spirit.
Love rebels not.
It only leaves the trodden way of ancient destinies for the
　　sacred grove,
To sing and dance its secret to eternity.

The week of May 5th *to* May 11th

The week of May 5th *to* May 11th

Thursday

Friday

The week of May 5th *to* May 11th

Saturday

Sunday

Death

Here I am, beautiful Death. Receive my spirit, reality of my dreams and substance of my hopes. Embrace me, beloved of my soul, for you are merciful and will not abandon me here. You are the messenger of the gods. You are the right hand of truth. Leave me not. How long have I sought you without finding, and called upon you and you hearkened not! But now have you heard me, therefore do not meet my love with shunning. Embrace my soul, my beloved Death.

The week of May 12th *to* May 18th

Monday

Tuesday

Wednesday

The week of May 12th *to* May 18th

Thursday

Friday

The week of May 12th *to* May 18th

Saturday

Sunday

According to One of the Marys

"His head was always high, and the flame of God was in His eyes.

"He was often sad, but His sadness was tenderness shown to those in pain, and comradeship given to the lonely.

"When He smiled His smile was as the hunger of those who long after the unknown. It was like the dust of stars falling upon the eyelids of children. And it was like a morsel of bread in the throat.

"He was sad, yet it was a sadness that would rise to the lips and become a smile.

"It was like a golden veil in the forest, when autumn is upon the world. And sometimes it seemed like moonlight upon the shores of the lake.

"He smiled as if His lips would sing at the wedding feast.

"Yet He was sad with the sadness of the wingèd who will not soar above his comrade."

The week of May 19th to May 25th

Monday

Tuesday

Wednesday

The week of May 19th to May 25th

Thursday

Friday

The week of May 19th *to* May 25th

Reason and Passion

Your reason and your passion are the rudder and the sails of your seafaring soul.

If either your sails or your rudder be broken, you can but toss and drift, or else be held at a standstill in mid-seas.

For reason, ruling alone, is a force confining; and passion, unattended, is a flame that burns to its own destruction.

Therefore let your soul exalt your reason to the height of passion, that it may sing;

And let it direct your passion with reason, that your passion may live through its own daily resurrection, and like the phoenix rise above its own ashes.

The week of May 26th to June 1st

Monday

Tuesday

Wednesday

The week of May 26th *to* June 1st

The week of May 26th to June 1st

Saturday

Sunday

They deem me mad because I will not sell my days for gold;
  And I deem them mad because they think my days
have a price.

The week of June 2nd to June 8th

Monday

Tuesday

Wednesday

The week of June 2nd *to* June 8th

Thursday

Friday

The week of June 2nd *to* June 8th

Beyond Wisdom and Folly

And call none among you foolish, for in truth we are
neither wise nor foolish. We are green leaves upon the
tree of life, and life itself is beyond wisdom, and surely
beyond foolishness.

The week of June 9th *to* June 15th

Monday

Tuesday

Wednesday

The week of June 9th *to* June 15th

Thursday

Friday

The week of June 9th *to* June 15th

Saturday

Sunday

The week of June 16th *to* June 22nd

The *week of* June 16th *to* June 22nd

Thursday

Friday

The week of June 16th *to* June 22nd

Saturday

Sunday

The Sacred Loom

The sacred loom is given you,
And the art to weave the fabric.
The loom and the art shall be yours forevermore,
And yours the dark thread and the light,
And yours the purple and the gold.
Yet you would grudge yourself a raiment.
Your hands have spun man's soul
From living air and fire,
Yet now you would break the thread,
And lend your versèd fingers to an idle eternity.

The week of June 23rd to June 29th

Monday

Tuesday

Wednesday

The week of June 23rd *to* June 29th

Thursday

Friday

The week of June 23rd *to* June 29th

The Playground of Life

A minute moving among the patterns of Beauty and the dreams of Love is greater and more precious than an age filled with splendor granted by the weak to the strong.

From that minute rises the god-state of man, and in that age it sleeps a deep sleep veiled by a veil of disturbing dreams;

In that minute is the spirit freed from the burdens of men's conflicting laws, and in that age is it prisoned behind walls of neglect and weighted with chains of oppression.

The week of June 30th to July 6th

Monday

Tuesday

Wednesday

The week of June 30th *to* July 6th

Thursday

Friday

The week of June 30th *to* July 6th

Saturday

Sunday

Nicodemus

Do you not remember me, Nicodemus, who believed in naught but the laws and decrees and was in continual subjection to observances?

And behold me now, a man who walks with life and laughs with the sun from the first moment it smiles upon the mountain until it yields itself to bed behind the hills.

The week of July 7th to July 13th

Monday

Tuesday

Wednesday

The week of July 7th *to* July 13th

Thursday

Friday

The week of July 7th *to* July 13th

Saturday

Sunday

My Friend

My friend, I am not what I seem. Seeming is but a garment I wear—a care-woven garment that protects me from thy questionings and thee from my negligence.

The "I" in me, my friend, dwells in the house of silence, and therein it shall remain forevermore, unperceived, unapproachable.

I would not have thee believe in what I say nor trust in what I do—for my words are naught but thy own thoughts in sound and my deeds thy own hopes in action.

When thou sayest, "The wind bloweth eastward," I say, "Aye, it doth blow eastward"; for I would not have thee know that my mind doth not dwell upon the wind but upon the sea.

The week of July 14th *to* July 20th

Monday

Tuesday

Wednesday

The week of July 14th *to* July 20th

The week of July 14th *to* July 20th

Saturday

Sunday

Freedom

You shall be free indeed not when your days are without a care nor your nights without a want and a grief,

But rather when these things girdle your life and yet you rise above them naked and unbound.

And how shall you rise beyond your days and nights unless you break the chains which you at the dawn of your understanding have fastened around your noon hour?

In truth, that which you call freedom is the strongest of these chains, though its links glitter in the sun and dazzle your eyes.

The week of July 21st to July 27th

Monday

Tuesday

Wednesday

The week of July 21st *to* July 27th

Thursday

Friday

The week of July 21st *to* July 27th

Saturday

Sunday

Faith is an oasis in the heart which will never be reached by the caravan of thinking.

The week of July 28th *to* August 3rd

The week of July 28th *to* August 3rd

Thursday

Friday

The week of July 28th to August 3rd

Saturday

Sunday

Man Is Born to Bondage

We, upon the heights, in man's sleep dream our dreams.
We urge his days to part from the valley of twilights
And seek their fullness upon the hills.
Our hands direct the tempests that sweep the world
And summon man from sterile peace to fertile strife,
And on to triumph.
In our eyes is the vision that turns man's soul to flame,
And leads him to exalted loneliness and rebellious
    prophecy,
And on to crucifixion.
Man is born to bondage,
And in bondage is his honor and his reward.

The week of August 4th *to* August 10th

Monday

Tuesday

Wednesday

The week of August 4th *to* August 10th

Friday

The week of August 4th *to* August 10th

The Golden Belt

Once upon a day two men who met on the road were walking together toward Salamis, the City of Columns. In mid-afternoon they came to a wide river and there was no bridge to cross it. They must needs swim, or seek another road unknown to them.

And they said to one another, "Let us swim. After all, the river is not so wide." And they threw themselves into the water and swam.

And one of the men, who had always known rivers and the way of rivers, in mid-stream suddenly began to lose himself, and to be carried away by the rushing waters; while the other, who had never swum before, crossed the river straightway and stood upon the farther bank. Then seeing his companion still wrestling with the stream, he threw himself again into the waters and brought him also safely to the shore.

And the man who had been swept away by the current said, "But you told me you could not swim. How then did you cross that river with such assurance?"

And the second man answered, "My friend, do you see this belt which girdles me? It is full of golden coins that I have earned for my wife and my children, a full year's work. It is the weight of this belt of gold that carried me across the river, to my wife and my children. And my wife and my children were upon my shoulders as I swam."

And the two men walked on together toward Salamis.

The week of August 11th *to* August 17th

Monday

Tuesday

Wednesday

Thursday

Friday

The week of August 11th *to* August 17th

The week of August 18th to August 24th

Monday

Tuesday

Wednesday

The week of August 18th to August 24th

The week of August 18th *to* August 24th

Saturday

Sunday

The Night of Knowledge

You grow in sleep, and live your fuller life in your dreaming. For all your days are spent in thanksgiving for that which you have received in the stillness of the night.

Oftentimes you think and speak of night as the season of rest, yet in truth night is the season of seeking and finding.

The day gives unto you the power of knowledge and teaches your fingers to become versed in the art of receiving; but it is night that leads you to the treasure house of Life.

The sun teaches to all things that grow their longing for the light; but it is night that raises them to the stars.

The week of August 25th to August 31st

Monday

Tuesday

Wednesday

The week of August 25th *to* August 31st

The week of August 25th *to* August 31st

Saturday

Sunday

The Old, Old Wine

Once there lived a rich man who was justly proud of his cellar and the wine therein. And there was one jug of ancient vintage kept for some occasion known only to himself.

The governor of the state visited him, and he bethought him and said, "That jug shall not be opened for a mere governor."

And a bishop of the diocese visited him, but he said to himself, "Nay, I will not open that jug. He would not know its value, nor would its aroma reach his nostrils."

The prince of the realm came and supped with him, but he thought, "It is too royal a wine for a mere princeling."

And even on the day when his own nephew was married, he said to himself, "No, not to these guests shall that jug be brought forth."

And the years passed by, and he died, an old man, and he was buried like unto every seed and acorn.

And upon the day that he was buried the ancient jug was brought out together with other jugs of wine, and it was shared by the peasants of the neighborhood. And none knew its great age.

To them, all that is poured into a cup is only wine.

The week of September 1st *to* September 7th

Monday

Tuesday

Wednesday

The week of September 1st *to* September 7th

Thursday

Friday

The week of September 1st to September 7th

Saturday

Sunday

I Will Wash Your Feet

And He spoke to the keeper of the inn and said, "Bring be a basin and a pitcher full of water, and a towel."

And He looked at us again and said gently, "Cast off your sandals."

We did not understand, but at His command we cast them off.

Then the keeper of the inn brought the basin and the pitcher; and Jesus said, "Now I will wash your feet. For I must needs free your feet from the dust of the ancient road, and give them the freedom of the new way."

The week of September 8th *to* September 14th

The week of September 8th *to* September 14th

Thursday

Friday

The week of September 8th *to* September 14th

Saturday

Sunday

A Glimpse into the Future

From beyond the wall of the Present I heard the praises of mankind.

I heard the voices of bells that shook the very air, heralding the commencement of prayer in the sanctuary of Beauty. Bells wrought by strength from the metal of feeling and raised above that holy shrine—the human heart.

The week of September 15th *to* September 21st

Monday

Tuesday

Wednesday

The week of September 15th *to* September 21st

Thursday

Friday

The week of September 15th to September 21st

Saturday

Sunday

Love

When love beckons to you, follow him,
  Though his ways are hard and steep.
  And when his wings enfold you, yield to him,
  Though the sword hidden among his pinions may wound you.
  And when he speaks to you, believe in him,
  Though his voice may shatter your dreams as the north wind lays waste the garden.

The week of September 22nd *to* September 28th

Monday

Tuesday

Wednesday

The week of September 22nd *to* September 28th

Thursday

Friday

The week of September 22nd *to* September 28th

Saturday

Sunday

Man

When out of chaos came the earth, and we, sons of the beginning, beheld each other in the lustless light, we breathed the first hushed, tremulous sound that quickened the currents of air and sea.

Then we walked, hand in hand, upon the gray infant world, and out of the echoes of our first drowsy steps time was born—a fourth divinity, that sets his feet upon our footprints, shadowing our thoughts and desires, and seeing only with our eyes.

And unto earth came life, and unto life came the spirit, the winged melody of the universe. And we ruled life and spirit, and none save us knew the measure of the years nor the weight of years' nebulous dreams, till we, at noontide of the seventh eon, gave the sea in marriage to the sun.

And from the inner chamber of their nuptial ecstasy we brought man, a creature who, though yielding and infirm, bears ever the marks of his parentage.

The *week of* September 29th *to* October 5th

Monday

Tuesday

Wednesday

The week of September 29th to October 5th

Thursday

Friday

The week of September 29th *to* October 5th

Saturday

Sunday

Autumn

Let us go to the vineyard, my love, and press the grapes and store the wine thereof in vessels as the spirit stores the wisdom of ages.

Let us gather the fruits and distill from the flowers their fragrance.

Let us return to the dwellings, for the leaves of the trees are become yellow and the winds have scattered them to make of them a burial shroud for flowers that died grieving at summer's passing.

Come, for the birds have taken flight to the seashore, bearing upon their wings the good cheer of the gardens, bequeathing desolation to the jasmine and the myrtle, and the last tears have been shed upon the sod.

The week of October 6th to October 12th

Monday

Tuesday

Wednesday

The week of October 6th *to* October 12th

The week of October 6th *to* October 12th

Saturday

Sunday

The Unheard Song

"And Life is veiled and hidden, even as your greater self is hidden and veiled. Yet when Life speaks, all the winds become words; and when she speaks again, the smiles upon your lips and the tears in your eyes turn also into words. When she sings, the deaf hear and are held; and when she comes walking, the sightless behold her and are amazed and follow her in wonder and astonishment."

And he ceased from speaking, and a vast silence enfolded the people, and in the silence there was an unheard song, and they were comforted of their loneliness and their aching.

The week of October 13th to October 19th

Monday

Tuesday

Wednesday

The week of October 13th *to* October 19th

Thursday

Friday

The week of October 13th *to* October 19th

Saturday

Sunday

Salome to a Woman Friend

He was like poplars shimmering in the sun;
And like a lake among the lonely hills,
Shining in the sun;
And like snow upon the mountain heights,
White, white in the sun.

Yea, He was like unto all these,
And I loved Him.
Yet I feared His presence.
And my feet would not carry my burden of love
That I might girdle His feet with my arms.

The week of October 20th to October 26th

Monday

Tuesday

Wednesday

The week of October 20th *to* October 26th

The week of October 20th *to* October 26th

Saturday

Sunday

The Soul

Say not, "I have found the truth," but rather, "I have found a truth."

Say not, "I have found the path of the soul." Say rather, "I have met the soul walking upon my path."

For the soul walks upon all paths.

The soul walks not upon a line, neither does it grow like a reed.

The soul unfolds itself, like a lotus of countless petals.

The week of October 27th to November 2nd

Monday

Tuesday

Wednesday

The week of October 27th *to* November 2nd

Thursday

Friday

The week of October 27th *to* November 2nd

Saturday

Sunday

Said a Sheet of Snow-white Paper...

Said a sheet of snow-white paper, "Pure was I created, and pure will I remain forever. I would rather be burnt and turn to white ashes than suffer darkness to touch me or the unclean to come near me."

The ink bottle heard what the paper was saying, and it laughed in its dark heart; but it never dared to approach her. And the multicolored pencils heard her also, and they too never came near her.

And the snow-white sheet of paper did remain pure and chaste forever—pure and chaste—and empty.

The week of November 3rd to November 9th

Monday

Tuesday

Wednesday

The week of November 3rd to November 9th

Thursday

Friday

Saturday

Sunday

The *week of* November 10th *to* November 16th

Monday

Tuesday

Wednesday

The week of November 10th *to* November 16th

Thursday

Friday

Saturday

Sunday

You see but your shadow when you turn your back to the sun.

The *week of* November 17th *to* November 23rd

Monday

Tuesday

Wednesday

The week of November 17th *to* November 23rd

Thursday

Friday

The week of November 17th *to* November 23rd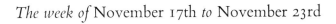

Saturday

Sunday

The Pomegranates

There was once a man who had many pomegranate trees in his orchard. And for many an autumn he would put his pomegranates on silvery trays outside of his dwelling, and upon the trays he would place signs upon which he himself had written, "Take one for aught. You are welcome."

But people passed by and no one took of the fruit.

Then the man bethought him, and one autumn he placed no pomegranates on silvery trays outside of his dwelling, but he raised this sign in large lettering: "Here we have the best pomegranates in the land, but we sell them for more silver than any other pomegranates."

And now behold, all the men and women of the neighborhood came rushing to buy.

The week of November 24th to November 30th

Monday

Tuesday

Wednesday

The week of November 24th *to* November 30th

Thursday

Friday

The week of November 24th *to* November 30th

Saturday

Sunday

Mercy

We are all climbing toward the summit of our hearts' desire. Should the other climber steal your sack and your purse and wax fat on the one and heavy on the other, you should pity him;

The climbing will be harder for his flesh, and the burden will make his way longer.

And should you in your leanness see his flesh puffing upward, help him a step; it will add to your swiftness.

The week of December 1st to December 7th

Monday

Tuesday

Wednesday

The week of December 1st to December 7th

Thursday

Friday

The week of December 1st *to* December 7th

Saturday

Sunday

The Vine of Man

We have planted man, our vine, and tilled the soil
In the purple mist of the first dawn.
We watched the lean branches grow,
And through the days of seasonless years
We nursed the infant leaves.
From the angry element we shielded the bud,
And against all dark spirits we guarded the flower.

The week of December 8th to December 14th

Monday

Tuesday

Wednesday

The week of December 8th *to* December 14th

The week of December 8th *to* December 14th

✦ *The Holy One* ✦

In every aspect of the day Jesus was aware of the Father. He beheld Him in the clouds and in the shadows of the clouds that pass over the earth. He saw the Father's face reflected in the quiet pools, and the faint print of His feet upon the sand; and He often closed His eyes to gaze into the Holy Eyes.

The night spoke to Him with the voice of the Father, and in solitude He heard the angel of the Lord calling to Him. And when He stilled Himself to sleep, He heard the whispering of the heavens in His dreams.

The week of December 15th *to* December 21st

The week of December 15th *to* December 21st

Thursday

Friday

The week of December 15th *to* December 21st

Saturday

Sunday

The week of December 22nd *to* December 28th

The week of December 22nd *to* December 28th

The week of December 22nd *to* December 28th

Your Neighbor

Your neighbor is your other self dwelling behind a wall. In understanding, all walls shall fall down.

Who knows but that your neighbor is your better self wearing another body? See that you love him as you would love yourself.

He too is a manifestation of the Most High, whom you do not know.

Your neighbor is a field where the springs of your hope walk in their green garments, and where the winters of your desire dream of snowy heights.

Your neighbor is a mirror wherein you shall behold your countenance made beautiful by a joy which you yourself did not know, and by a sorrow you yourself did not share.

The week of December 29th to January 4th

The week of December 29th *to* January 4th

Thursday

Friday

The week of December 29th *to* January 4th

Saturday

Sunday

A Note on the Type

The text of this book has been set on the Monotype in a type face named Bembo. The roman is a copy of a letter cut for the celebrated Venetian printer Aldus Manutius by Francesco Griffo, and first used in Cardinal Bembo's *De Aetna* of 1495—hence the name of the revival. Griffo's type is now generally recognized, thanks to the researches of Mr. Stanley Morison, to be the first of the old face group of types. The companion italic is an adaptation of a chancery script type designed by the Roman calligrapher and printer Lodovico degli Arrighi, called Vincentino, and used by him during the 1520's.

The book was printed by Halliday Lithograph Corp., West Hanover, Mass., and bound by The Colonial Press, Inc., Clinton, Mass. Typography and binding design by CLINT ANGLIN.